Elements

LEAD AND TIN

Pb   Sn

Grolier Educational

SHERMAN TURNPIKE, DANBURY, CONNECTICUT 06816

How to use this book

This book has been carefully developed to help you understand the chemistry of the elements. In it you will find a systematic and comprehensive coverage of the basic qualities of each element. Each two-page entry contains information at various levels of technical content and language, along with definitions of useful technical terms, as shown in the thumbnail diagram to the right. There is a comprehensive glossary of technical terms at the back of the book, along with an extensive index, key facts, an explanation of the periodic table, and a description of how to interpret chemical equations.

The main text follows the sequence of information in the book and summarizes the concepts presented on the two pages.

Technical definitions.

Substatements flesh out the ideas in the main text with more fact and specific explanation.

Equations are written as symbols and sometimes given as "ball-and-stick" diagrams – see page 48.

Photographs and diagrams have been carefully selected and annotated for clarity.

Also… explains advanced concepts.

. . . .

Author
Brian Knapp, BSc, PhD
Project consultant
Keith B. Walshaw, MA, BSc, DPhil
        (Head of Chemistry, Leighton Park School)
Industrial consultant
Jack Brettle, BSc, PhD (Chief Research Scientist, Pilkington plc)
Art Director
Duncan McCrae, BSc
Editor
Elizabeth Walker, BA
Special photography
Ian Gledhill
Illustrations
David Woodroffe
Designed and produced by
EARTHSCAPE EDITIONS
Print consultants
Landmark Production Consultants Ltd
Reproduced by
Leo Reprographics
Printed and bound by
Paramount Printing Company Ltd

First published in the United States in 1996 by Grolier Educational, Sherman Turnpike, Danbury, CT 06816

Cataloging information may be obtained directly from Grolier Educational.

Set ISBN 0–7172–7572–8
Volume ISBN 0–7172–7582–5
Library of Congress Number: 95–082222

Acknowledgments
The publishers would like to thank the following for their kind help and advice: *Dr Angus McCrae, Charles Schotman and Jonathan Frankel of J.M. Frankel and Associates.*

Picture credits
All photographs are from the **Earthscape Editions** photolibrary except the following:
(c=center t=top b=bottom l=left r=right)
Mary Evans Picture Library 17, 31; **Tony Waltham, Geophotos** 12–13; **UKAEA** 27 and **ZEFA** 6, 36–37.

Front cover: Lead monoxide being reduced to molten lead by heating in the presence of carbon in the form of a block.
Title page: Because lead is malleable and unreactive, it is ideal for holding a complex pattern of irregularly shaped glass pieces together to make this beautiful leaded window.

This product is manufactured from sustainable managed forests. For every tree cut down at least one more is planted.

The demonstrations described or illustrated in this book are not for replication. The Publisher cannot accept any responsibility for any accidents or injuries that may result from conducting the experiments described or illustrated in this book.

Contents

Introduction

An element is a substance that cannot be broken down into a simpler substance by any known means. Each of the 92 naturally occurring elements is therefore one of the fundamental materials from which everything in the Universe is made. This book is about the elements lead and tin.

Lead

You have probably noticed the word lead most commonly in gas stations. Here much of the fuel is called lead-free, or unleaded. This tells us two important things about lead: it is very useful (otherwise lead would not have been put in gas), and it has unpleasant side effects (otherwise why would such a fuss be made of taking lead *out* of gas?).

In fact, people have always had a love–hate relationship with this important and commonly used metal. For example, lead was used by ancient peoples to make coloring pigments (often white) for paints. More disastrously, they also used lead in cosmetics. From this kind of use lead was absorbed into the body, where it acted as a poison. Lead in gas could also have a similar effect, which is why it is now not used in fuels. But lead is also waterproof, easy to shape and does not corrode. It was just the thing for making water pipes – until it was discovered that lead dissolves in soft water and so contaminates the water.

The chemical symbol for lead is Pb. This is derived from *plumbum*, the Latin word for lead.

▲ Snail-eating utensils cast in pewter.

Perhaps the most confusing thing about this soft gray metal is that one of the most common uses we can think of for lead – for pencils – is not actually lead. Pencil "lead" is made from a form of carbon called graphite. In fact, if a pencil contained real lead, it would be very heavy to pick up, because lead is one of the heaviest metals on Earth.

Tin

The chemical symbol for tin is Sn, which comes from the Latin word *stannum*. It has many properties similar to lead; for example, it is a soft, weak metal and unreactive like lead.

Tin is found associated with copper and, like zinc, it has a low melting point. Tin was probably first used by ancient civilizations accidentally combined with copper. In this way they discovered bronze, the metal that gave its name to the period of ancient history called the Bronze Age.

Tin metal quickly develops an invisible protective coating when exposed to air. For this reason it has been used as a plating for protecting metals such as iron. But, because tin is less reactive than iron, tin is not an ideal material for protecting steel, and tin plate has been replaced by aluminum in many canning applications.

Tin is mainly found in alloys, including solders used in electronic circuits. Its other important role is as a liquid bed for the production of the sheet glass used for window panes, known as float glass.

Lead minerals

Lead forms a natural compound with many other elements, but it is most commonly seen as crystals of lead sulfide, where it is known as the mineral galena. It is a very heavy mineral, about three times as dense as most rocks.

Galena forms crystals that are shaped like cubes with a dull gray (lead gray) color. The crystals are soft for a mineral, about the same hardness as a fingernail. This is why galena will mark surfaces with a dull gray line.

▼ The location of hydrothermal deposits in fissures above a magma source.

Layers of sedimentary rocks are pushed up by the rising magma.

Hydrothermal veins in which minerals are concentrated.

Magma from below the Earth's crust initially heats the surrounding rocks but eventually cools to form granite.

Rocks around the hot magma chamber are metamorphosed or changed.

▼ Lead ore being mined. Here a drill is being used to make holes for explosives to blast the tunnel face. The tunnel is following the metamorphosed rock that surrounds a fissure.

Where lead is found

Lead is widespread, occurring in the same location as other metals such as gold, silver and zinc. It mainly occurs as the mineral galena (lead sulfide, PbS) and also as cerussite (lead carbonate, $PbCO_3$) and anglesite (lead sulfate, $PbSO_4$).

Most concentrated metal deposits are formed in hydrothermal veins, that is, fissures in rocks sited above magma chambers. As hot mineral-rich fluids rise from the magma chambers during the last stages of volcanic activity, the fluids cool and a number of minerals solidify, among them lead. For this reason, ore mines usually recover a variety of metals.

Lead mines are sometimes found in areas of limestones (especially a form called dolomite) that once had magma chambers below them. Limestones have many natural fissures through which hot minerals can easily flow.

density: the mass per unit volume (e.g., g/cc).

hydrothermal: a process in which hot water is involved. It is usually used in the context of rock formation because hot water and other fluids sent outward from liquid magmas are important carriers of metals and the minerals that form gemstones.

magma: the molten rock that forms a balloon-shaped chamber in the rock below a volcano. It is fed by rock moving upward from below the crust.

mineral: a solid substance made of just one element or chemical compound. Calcite is a mineral because it consists only of calcium carbonate; halite is a mineral because it contains only sodium chloride; quartz is a mineral because it consists of only silicon dioxide.

sulfide: a sulfur compound that contains no oxygen.

vein: a mineral deposit different from, and usually cutting across, the surrounding rocks. Most mineral and metal-bearing veins are deposits filling fractures. The veins were filled by hot, mineral-rich waters rising upward from liquid volcanic magma. They are important sources of many metals, such as silver and gold, and also minerals such as gemstones. Veins are usually narrow and were best suited to hand-mining. They are less exploited in the modern machine age.

◄ The cubic structure and dull gray color of lead sulfide shows very clearly in this specimen.

▼ Lead metal is bluish, but it readily oxidizes in the presence of air to a dull gray. In polluted air it turns dark gray to black.

Galena

Lead sulfide, or galena, is easily spotted by its dark gray cubic (box-shaped) crystals.

Galena is soft. When it is rubbed against a surface, it leaves a gray streak of color, showing its lead content. Like other lead compounds, galena is very heavy.

Galena is the main source of lead for the world's industries.

Refining lead in the laboratory

Lead ore normally occurs as an oxide or a sulfide. On these pages you can see a laboratory demonstration of the principle of refining the ore. You can then compare this with the industrial processing shown on pages 10 and 11. In this demonstration an orange form of lead monoxide (lead II oxide, PbO) is used, known as litharge.

To produce lead from its ore, the ore is first reduced (its oxygen removed) by placing it in a hollowed-out carbon block. The hollowing is important because the molten lead metal needs to be contained as the demonstration progresses.

Lead has a low melting point, so this demonstration proceeds under the heat of an ordinary Bunsen flame.

❷▼ The carbon block reduces some of the oxide and forms a molten globule of lead metal. Colorless carbon monoxide gas is given off during this reaction.

❶▼ Lead monoxide powder is heated on a carbon block.

EQUATION: Reduction of lead monoxide

Lead monoxide + carbon ⇨ lead + carbon monoxide

$$2PbO(s) \quad + \quad 2C(s) \quad ⇨ \quad 2Pb(s) \quad + \quad 2CO(g)$$

❸▶ The molten globule cools to leave solid lead.

ore: a rock containing enough of a useful substance to make mining it worthwhile.

oxide: a compound that includes oxygen and one other element.

reduction: the removal of oxygen from a substance.

reducing agent: a substance that gives electrons to another substance. Carbon is a reducing agent when heated with lead oxide.

Molten lead globule

Processing lead ore

Most lead is recovered from lead sulfide ore. The first stage of processing involves the concentration of the ore and the removal of sulfur. The ore contains a variety of other elements, each of which has to be removed.

Because of the various impurities, lead is refined in a number of stages. Each stage depends on the contrast between the chemical and physical properties of lead and those of the other elements.

Processing lead ore

Lead ore is concentrated by crushing it to a fine powder and placing it into a vat with about three times as much water that contains wetting and frothing chemicals.

Air is introduced into the vat, causing the frothing agents to make bubbles. The chemicals prevent the metal from becoming wet and metal grains are caught up by air bubbles, float, and can be skimmed off.

Flotation increases the concentration of metal to about three-fifths. At this concentration the ore can be roasted – a process called sintering – which removes any sulfur as sulfur dioxide gas, leaving lead oxide behind. The byproduct of the sintering operation, sulfur dioxide gas, is usually converted to sulfuric acid and sold.

Next, the lead oxide is smelted with a supply of coke and limestone in a furnace. The coke is almost pure carbon, and the reaction reduces the lead oxide to lead and forms carbon monoxide gas. The limestone forms a slag with some other impurities, and the metal flows free. It is tapped off the furnace and made into ingots.

The ingots make "base bullion." This is not pure lead but contains small amounts of other metals. These are separated out and recovered when the lead is purified by the Parkes process (described opposite).

▼ Stages in the Parkes process.

❶ Impure lead ingot is melted and allowed to cool until the copper can be skimmed off.

❷ The lead is reheated and air blown through it. More impurities oxidize, form a slag, and can be skimmed off.

❸ Some zinc is added, and the alloy that forms contains zinc, silver and gold. These are skimmed off.

❹ The lead is finally purified by making it the anode of an electrolysis cell; pure lead collects at the cathode.

EQUATION: Removal of sulfur in lead sulfide ore by heating

Lead sulfide + oxygen ⇨ lead monoxide + sulfur dioxide

$$2PbS(s) \quad + \quad 3O_2(g) \quad ⇨ \quad 2PbO(s) \quad + \quad 2SO_2(g)$$

Refining lead by the Parkes process

In the Parkes process, contaminating elements are removed in a number of stages designed to allow the recovery of the impurities (which are themselves often valuable) as well as the lead.

Ingots of lead are melted and then allowed to cool. Copper has a higher melting point than lead, so as the mixture cools, crystals of copper float to the surface and can be skimmed off.

The lead is then reheated and a blast of air shot through it. This oxidizes elements such as arsenic, and the oxides form a slag that can be skimmed off.

The next stage involves removing the silver and gold with a small amount of zinc. The silver and gold are more soluble than lead in zinc, so they alloy with the zinc. Zinc alloy is less dense that lead, so it rises to the surface and can be skimmed off. In this way zinc, silver and gold are all removed.

The remaining material, which is already nearly pure lead, can be further refined by electrolysis. An impure lead slab is used as the anode and a pure lead slab as the cathode. As the current flows, lead ions are attracted to the cathode of the cell and electroplated on it. When the cathode has accumulated sufficient lead, it is removed and replaced. The impurities on the anode consist mainly of valuable bismuth, and they, too, are collected.

alloy: a mixture of a metal and various other elements.

electrode: a conductor that forms one terminal of a cell.

electrolysis: an electrical-chemical process that uses an electric current to cause the breakup of a compound and the movement of metal ions in a solution. The process happens in many natural situations (as for example in rusting) and is also commonly used in industry for purifying (refining) metals or for plating metal objects with a fine, even metal coating.

electrolyte: a solution that conducts electricity.

gangue: the unwanted material in an ore.

oxidation: a reaction in which the oxidizing agent removes electrons. (Note that oxidizing agents do not have to contain oxygen.)

pyrometallurgy: refining a metal from its ore using heat. A blast furnace or smelter is the main equipment used.

slag: a mixture of substances that are waste products of a furnace. Most slags are composed mainly of silicates.

▼ This diagram shows the principle of the froth flotation process.

Air

Water, oil, detergent and ore mixture

Mineral particles suspended in froth

Froth separation

Oil and detergent recycled

Desired product

Gangue

Lead mine pollution

Lead has been mined throughout the world for centuries. However, until recently the process was not very efficient. For the most part, the ore was simply roasted to remove the sulfur, the sulfur dioxide being allowed to escape to the environment. As a result, lead smelting was a significant cause of air pollution and acid rain.

Furthermore, the gangue, which was simply piled up near to the mines, still contained considerable quantities of lead.

Lead compounds can be toxic to plants as well as animals. As a result, little will grow on many of the spoil heaps left from decades of inefficient mining.

Because lead dissolves very slowly in water, it will take a very long time for the lead to be washed from the upper part of the waste heaps and for vegetation to recolonize the ground. Without positive conservation measures, such pollution will remain to scar the landscape for centuries.

◀ Leadville, Colorado, was named after the lead deposits found at the site where the town grew up. It is in the Rocky Mountains, a site of former volcanic activity that is underlain by ancient granites.

The barren land in the foreground of this picture shows part of the spoil and also places where the ore was roasted. The area remains barren a century after most mining ceased.

The only way the land can be reclaimed is for the contaminated surface material to be removed and transferred to pits elsewhere. A start has recently been made on such reclamation using federal funds.

▼ Lead sulfide processing in China. This modern picture shows that much of the ore recovery is still done by simple roasting techniques, allowing the sulfur gases to escape to the environment, while the waste rock containing lead still accumulates over the landscape.

dissolve: to break down a substance in a solution without reacting.

toxic: poisonous enough to cause death.

Lead metal

Lead is the heaviest of all the common metals. It is over 11 times as heavy as an equal volume of water. It is a plentiful (and therefore cheap) material, whose unreactive properties make it useful for a wide range of applications. For example, it has been used for sculpture because it can be cast accurately.

The denseness of lead makes it a very useful material where compact weight is needed. You will find small pieces of lead sewn into the lower hem of some curtains to make them hang straight, and you will find lead in the bottom (keel) of a ship to balance the weight of the superstructure and to help stop it from rolling over. Lead, which is soft and will absorb shocks, can also be used as mounting blocks for heavy machines to help damp down vibrations.

Lead will also absorb radiation, and it has an important application in protecting radiographers and unexposed film from X-rays.

▲ Lead has a low melting point and can be used to make alloys suitable for fuse wires.

▼ Many lead compounds are insoluble. They are also heavy and readily settle out as soon as they have been precipitated. The tiny granules of the precipitate can be seen as they settle to the bottom of the test tube. The only common soluble lead compounds are lead nitrate and lead acetate.

Lead shot

For a long time small pieces of lead – called lead shot – were used by fishermen and clipped onto the line below a float to hold the float and tackle in the correct position in the water. This was banned after it was discovered that birds ate the shot and got lead poisoning.

For many centuries lead has also been used to make the shot that was loaded into guns. It was an ideal material, easily made molten, heavy and yet small, so it could easily travel through the air with the minimum loss of speed.

Lead shot is made by pouring molten lead from the top of a high tower. As the lead falls, it breaks up into tiny globules that solidify in the cool air. The lead reaches the bottom of the tower as round lead shot, where its fall is broken in a tub of water or oil.

Like most bases, lead hydroxide is insoluble. This granular precipitate of lead hydroxide was made by reacting solutions of lead nitrate and sodium hydroxide.

density: the mass per unit volume (e.g., g/cc).

radiation: the exchange of energy with the surroundings through the transmission of waves or particles of energy. Radiation is a form of energy transfer that can happen through space; no intervening medium is required (as would be the case for conduction and convection).

X-rays: a form of very shortwave radiation.

◀▲▶ Lead shot (small balls of lead) is widely used as weights in floats. In these examples the base of the float is weighted with lead shot so that the float stands upright in the liquid. In this way the float can be used as a hydrometer, a device for measuring the density of a liquid. The picture above shows the hydrometer in pure water; the one on the right shows it in salt water.

Lead ammunition

Lead is a suitable material for ammunition because it is heavy, cheap and easily formed into a shape. In this application its toxic chemical qualities are of no concern, for obvious reasons.

Lead-only bullets are made of lead alloyed with antimony. The cold alloy is sometimes forced through a die to make the correct bullet shape, or hot metal is poured into a mold. Lead deforms as it moves through the air, so lead bullets are used only in .22 caliber ammunition and in target-shooting handguns.

Ammunition used in high-velocity rifles has a lead–antimony core but is jacketed in brass or copper so that it keeps its shape.

Reactivity of lead

Many metals are subject to corrosion when placed in air or soil that is damp. The more reactive elements, such as sodium, cannot be used at all. Others that are quite reactive, such as iron, need to be protected by covering them in a protective coating of, say, paint.

Metal elements that are not very reactive can find many useful applications in weather-beaten environments or where resistance to corrosion by water is needed.

All metal elements can be placed in order of their reactivity with other elements. The list of the more common metal elements is shown on this page. Those that are most reactive (and that can rarely be used in air or water) are at the top of the list, while those that can withstand exposure to air and water indefinitely are at the bottom of the list. Chemists call this list of elements the reactivity series.

You can see from the list on the right that only the precious metals (gold, silver, platinum) and mercury and copper are more resistant to corrosion than lead. The precious metals are too rare to have any wide use. This is why lead and copper have been so widely used for water systems and other locations exposed to possible corrosion. Lead has a low melting point, is cheap, and sheets can easily be formed into special shapes by hand, whereas copper is not as easily formed, is more expensive, and has to be beaten into shape.

REACTIVITY SERIES	
Element	Reactivity
potassium	most reactive
sodium	
calcium	
magnesium	
aluminum	
manganese	
chromium	
zinc	
iron	
cadmium	
tin	
lead	
copper	
mercury	
silver	
gold	
platinum	least reactive

▲ Lead is found toward the bottom of the reactivity series.

► Lead and lead-based alloys are frequently used as part of the protective sheathing for buried electricity cables. The lead is not only noncorrosive, but being soft, it will bend.

The lead alloy shown here is corrugated for extra strength and flexibility as it is extruded from the cable-making machine. Dense, soft lead will help to absorb damage that might be accidentally produced later by, for example, a mechanical digger reworking the site of the buried cable.

corrosion: the *slow* decay of a substance resulting from contact with gases and liquids in the environment. The term is often applied to metals. Rust is the corrosion of iron.

inert: nonreactive.

precious metal: silver, gold, platinum, iridium and palladium. Each is prized for its rarity. This category is the equivalent of gemstones for minerals.

pyrite: "mineral of fire." This name comes from the fact that pyrite (iron sulfide) will give off sparks if struck with a stone.

Lead containers

Why would you want to make a container out of one of the world's heaviest metals? The answer lies in a key property of lead: it will not corrode. So, for just the same reason as it was once useful for making water pipes, lead was traditionally used to make containers.

When a container is made from lead, the surface atoms of the lead react with the oxygen in the air to make lead oxide. When lead comes into contact with sulfuric acid, it makes an inert coating of lead sulfate.

Normally, it is very difficult to find containers for sulfuric acid because it dissolves them; but because lead reacts very slowly to form a protective coating of lead sulfate, sulfuric acid can readily be kept in lead. In fact, you may well find a lead-lined tub of sulfuric acid in some school metal workshops, where the acid is used for removing the oxide from most metals.

Lead chamber process

The lead chamber process was the earliest method of preparing sulfuric acid. Its development was one of the landmarks in the development of industrial chemistry because it allowed a valuable raw material, sulfuric acid, to be produced in large quantities for the first time. This, in turn, allowed the acid to be produced much more economically than previously and so brought down the price of chemicals and the processes and products that depended on them.

The lead chambers were the size of rooms. In this process a mixture of sulfur or pyrite and potassium nitrate was placed in a ladle and ignited. The floor of the chamber was covered with water. As the mixture burned, the gases produced condensed on the inside of the lead-lined chamber and were absorbed by the water.

The process produced about two-thirds purity sulfuric acid. The purpose of the lead chambers was simply to act as an inert container (since the lead forms an insoluble sulfate coating when in contact with the sulfuric acid).

Lead oxides

Lead oxides produce a variety of colors. For example, the most important oxide of lead (called litharge) is an orange substance used in a wide variety of applications. A mixture of litharge and red lead is used as the active coating on the plates of all lead–acid batteries (see page 28). It can be used in glass-making to produce glass that will prevent the penetration of X-rays and other radioactive sources.

The distinctive color of litharge is used in pottery glazes and enamels and as a toughener in rubber. Made into chrome yellow, it is incorporated into some paints.

Lead oxide is also important when dissolved in sodium hydroxide, where it acts to break up some sulfur compounds in petroleum refineries.

Red lead is used in some paints designed to prevent iron and steel from corroding (see page 24).

▶ Lead oxides make a variety of colors. Massicot is a yellow form of lead monoxide (lead II oxide or PbO). Lead monoxide is one of the most widely used and commercially important metallic compounds. The bright orange-red powder is known as "red lead" (Pb_3O_4), whereas the darkest powder is lead dioxide (lead IV oxide, PbO_2).

EQUATION: Oxidation of lead

Lead + oxygen ⇨ lead monoxide (litharge)

$$2Pb(s) + O_2(g) \Rightarrow 2PbO(s)$$

Red lead

Red lead is an example of a mixed oxide. Although its formula is Pb_3O_4, it behaves chemically as though it were a mixture of lead monoxide (lead II oxide, PbO) and lead dioxide (lead IV oxide, PbO_2). When it is heated, it decomposes to lead monoxide and releases oxygen.

EQUATION: Heating red lead to release oxygen

Red lead ⇨ lead monoxide + oxygen

$$2Pb_3O_4(s) \Rightarrow 6PbO(s) + O_2(g)$$

decompose: to break down a substance (for example, by heat or with the aid of a catalyst) into simpler components. In such a chemical reaction only one substance is involved.

oxidation: a reaction in which the oxidizing agent removes electrons. (Note that oxidizing agents do not have to contain oxygen.)

oxide: a compound that includes oxygen and one other element.

Lead nitrate and sulfide

Lead is not a very reactive metal, and the compounds it forms are therefore not very stable. As a result it is relatively easy to get lead compounds to break down, or decompose.

Some lead compounds also have photoelectric properties, that is, they will change their conductivity when infrared light reaches them.

Both of these properties are demonstrated on these pages.

Lead sulfide as a photoconductor

When some lead compounds absorb light, electrons are freed, making them more conductive. Lead sulfide (PbS), lead selenide (PbSe) and lead telluride (PbTe) are all sensitive to infrared radiation (although they are not sensitive to visible light).

Each of these photoconducting substances finds a role in detecting infrared radiation. For example, photoconductors can detect the infrared radiation given out by warm bodies. It is for this reason that they are used to make PIR (Passive infrared) detectors, now commonplace as part of home security. They are used to trigger alarms or switch on lights when a warm body (such as a person or a vehicle) comes within their detection range.

▲ A PIR detector containing a lead sulfide photoconductor.

Also:

Cadmium sulfide is sensitive to changes in visible light, and it is the semiconducting material used in dusk-to-dawn light switches and camera photocells.

Decomposition of lead nitrate

Lead nitrate decompose to lead oxide when it is heated. As the lead nitrate decomposes, energy is released, and the crystals of lead nitrate break up. The process of breaking down is called decrepitation; it produces a loud crackling sound.

Decrepitation releases both nitrogen dioxide and oxygen, the gases collected at the left-hand end of the apparatus.

❶▼ The apparatus set up before the experiment

decompose: to break down a substance (for example, by heat or with the aid of a catalyst) into simpler components. In such a chemical reaction only one substance is involved.

electron: a tiny, negatively charged particle that is part of an atom. The flow of electrons through a solid material such as a wire produces an electric current.

infrared radiation: a form of light radiation in which the wavelength of the waves is slightly longer than visible light. Most heat radiation is in the infrared band.

❷◀ Lead nitrate is heated, releasing gases and producing crackling sounds.

Lead nitrate, a white powder, being heated. It changes color as it melts and decomposes to lead oxide. The bubbles and the brown fumes are oxygen gas and nitrogen oxides.

❸▼ A closeup of the decomposition of lead nitrate.

Bunsen burner

EQUATION: Decomposition of lead nitrate

Lead nitrate ⇨ lead monoxide + nitrogen dioxide + oxygen

$$2Pb(NO_3)_2(s) \quad ⇨ \quad 2PbO(s) \quad + \quad 4NO_2(g) \quad + \quad O_2(g)$$

Lead for buildings

Lead has many natural advantages for building. It has been widely used in the past and continues to be used today.

Lead's properties are ideal for building: it is waterproof, soft and easily molded into awkward corners that cannot be filled by other materials. It is heavy, holding the roof of a building down even in high winds, and it does not corrode, so a lead roof will remain in good repair for many centuries.

In the Middle Ages most cathedral roofs in Europe were made of sheet lead, which is why they have a dull gray appearance. The lead roof of a cathedral in Istanbul, Turkey, is known to have lasted without repair for over 1,400 years.

Lead is also used for protecting buried cables and for sealing castiron pipes in some sewage systems.

Lead in water systems

The word plumbing is derived from the Latin word for lead, *plumbum*. For many centuries people did not have any idea that lead was a danger to health. They could not detect the minute amounts of lead compounds that dissolved in water, and so people could only see the advantages of the metal.

One of the main needs was to get water from rivers or reservoirs to homes inside cities. The Romans were one of the first civilizations to achieve this, carrying water cross-country in long stone aqueducts. However, these open waterways were of no use in the city; instead, pipes were needed to bring water to homes. Some pipes were made of naturally hollow materials such as bamboo or cast materials such as clay, but most pipes were molded from lead because it was soft, did not corrode, and could be easily shaped to go around bends and other difficult areas of buildings. One pipe could also be joined to another very easily.

Although the Romans were the first to use them, lead water pipes continued to be used for most plumbing systems well into the present century. It was only quite recently that the possible dangers of lead in pipes became known. Today millions of homes are still supplied by water through lead pipes.

Also:

There are many, and sometimes confusing, uses of the word lead in connection with glass. The earliest use may be when, in about 1675, the English glassmaker Ravenscroft developed "glass of lead" that was more durable than the glass then being made. Lead crystal is glass containing enough lead to alter the refractive index, while leaded glass refers to the way glass panes are fixed with lead strips.

corrosion: the *slow* decay of a substance resulting from contact with gases and liquids in the environment. The term is often applied to metals.

◄ Lead was a common roofing material for grand buildings because it could readily be molded into shape. Beginning with St Sofia in Instanbul, the fashion for leaded domes spread across Europe. This picture is of Venice.

Lead is used more sparingly on modern buildings, but it still has an important function as lead flashing. The soft lead sheet is let into the brick courses and then laid out and molded over the top edge of a window. This provides an easily laid, long-lasting and waterproof seal for the top of the window.

Leaded glass

In the past it was only possible to make small panes of glass. As a result, some means of joining them together had to be found. This is why many old windows were made of panes of glass held together with strips of lead.

Lead is soft and was easily molded around the panes. Lead also melts at temperatures far below that of glass and so could be melted to run into the window frames and seal the glass.

(Modern frames use diamond leading that is simply stuck onto the outside of the pane for decoration. It serves no other purpose.)

◄ Traditional diamond leaded windows as used in the original Maryland State House complex.

Lead in paint and glaze

A paint is a liquid that is applied to a surface to protect it and to give it a color. A paint is made up of solid coloring material – known as a pigment – mixed into a liquid that allows the pigment to be applied with a brush or spray gun. When it is applied, the liquid evaporates or reacts chemically with the surface, leaving the pigment behind as a thin solid film.

One of the most common pigments used in paint was white lead, a general term for a range of white lead pigments such as lead carbonate, lead sulfate and lead silicate. For many years it was used in interior gloss paints and in exterior paints; but because of the possibility that very young children might eat the paint, it is no longer used for interior or domestic purposes.

The other colored oxides of lead have also been widely used. Red-leaded paints are still used for exterior applications because lead oxide and lead silicates are so stable they resist corrosion even in the most exposed places. Red lead is still widely used as a metal–protective undercoat.

▼ Red lead being applied as a protective coat after a rusty part has been stabilized with phosphoric acid.

The drying properties of lead

When a paint has been applied, it is still liquid, and the faster it can be made to dry, the more attractive it will be. The first phase of the drying occurs when the solvent used to apply the pigment evaporates.

But often a further chemical reaction is needed to make the paint into a hard solid. Many paints – gloss paints, for example – use an oil base. In these cases hardening ("drying") occurs as the oil polymerizes on exposure to air, forming long chains of material that can no longer move about.

These setting processes are speeded up by the use of a catalyst. Several metals, including lead, have been widely used as drying additives.

catalyst: a substance that speeds up a chemical reaction but itself remains unaltered at the end of the reaction.

ceramic: a material based on clay minerals which has been heated so that it has chemically hardened.

flux: a material used to make it easier for a liquid to flow. A flux dissolves metal oxides and so prevents a metal from oxidizing while being heated.

pigment: any solid material used to give a liquid a color.

Lead glaze

The shiny, smooth glasslike finish on many pots and other ceramic objects is called a glaze. Color and decoration are also added to the glaze, while the hard smooth finish makes the finished ceramic object much easier to wash and clean.

The glaze is made from powdered glass mixed with a coloring material. Lead oxide is a common coloring substance. Powdered glass and lead oxide are mixed in water and then coated on the pot or other object. The glaze is then dried and heated in a kiln to make the glass powder soften and form a continuous coating, and thus fix the glaze in place. At the same time, the glaze reacts chemically with the ceramic and so forms a permanent bond.

The lead oxide has two roles. It adds a white color to the glaze, and at the same time, it lowers the temperature at which the glaze melts and ensures that it runs more smoothly while in the kiln. This property of a material makes it an efficient flux.

▶ Lead is a common component of glaze, the reflective surface coating on pottery.

Lead and glass

Glass is one of the most common materials we use. It is formed from sand with additional compounds such as soda (sodium carbonate), limestone and lead. It is heated to about 1,300°C, when the reactants chemically combine to produce glass (and give off gaseous products).

The Venetians were the first to add lead to the glass-making mixture. The lead allows the glass to be molded over a wider range of temperatures. This, in turn, allowed the Venetians to make glass in more complicated shapes.

However, the lead-containing glass called crystal was developed in England in the 17th century. The use of lead made the glass even clearer and therefore more transparent. Also, the lead changed the optical properties of the glass, giving cut glass a special sparkle. This helped to make London the foremost glass-making center of the 18th century.

▲ Lead glass (crystal)

The effect of lead additives

Most glasses are a form of silica made from a network of silica molecules. In quartz these molecules are packed together in a regular framework; but when other atoms, such as sodium, calcium or lead, are added, the rigid framework is somewhat broken up. This is what makes glass less viscous than molten quartz, and why it also melts at lower temperatures.

Lead makes glass sparkle because it changes the optical properties of the glass, increasing the refractive index of the glass and thus increasing the reflectivity. A traditional lead crystal glass contains (by weight) about 56% silica, 30% lead oxide, 2% sodium oxide and 12% potassium oxide.

Optical glass, for example, glass used in lenses, has a broad spectrum of lead content, the amount varying between 3 and 70% depending on the refractive index required.

Lead also has the ability to absorb radiation, so optical glass with a high lead content (64% lead oxide, 27% silica) is used for remote viewing of X-ray facilities, hot cells in nuclear research, irradiation facilities for food preservation and medical sterilization installations.

▶ Lead glasses have about half the radiation absorption capability compared with lead sheet of the same thickness, which is why the glass is usually made thicker than the remaining lead shielding.

Solder glasses

A variety of lead glasses are important as low-melting sealing and solder glasses. A solder glass is a piece of glass used to join two pieces of glass together. This may be important, for example, in joining two intricate shapes or when sealing glasses to metals, as in the manufacture of television tubes.

For these purposes a low-softening-point glass is needed so that the solder glass can be softened and used at temperatures well below the softening points of the two pieces of glass that are to be joined. This glass will soften at about 630°C. A typical sealing glass contains about 23% lead oxide by weight. (Glass used for fine lead crystal contains about 30% lead oxide by weight.)

bond: chemical bonding is either a transfer or sharing of electrons by two or more atoms. There are a number of types of chemical bond, some very strong (such as covalent bonds), others weak (such as hydrogen bonds).

oxide: a compound that includes oxygen and one other element.

refractive index: the property of a transparent material that controls the angle at which total internal reflection will occur. The greater the refractive index, the more reflective the material.

viscous: slow-moving, syrupy. A liquid that has a low viscosity is said to be mobile.

Lead in batteries

One of the biggest users of lead and lead oxide is the storage battery industry. The main plates used in lead–acid batteries are made from grids of lead alloy, alternate plates being coated with "spongy" lead and lead oxide.

The lead–acid battery is made of a number of units, each called cells. Every cell in a lead–acid battery can generate approximately 2 volts of electricity. In a car battery six cells are placed in series, producing a total of about 12 volts.

Bubbles of gas seen during charging are due to the splitting of some water molecules into oxygen and hydrogen gases.

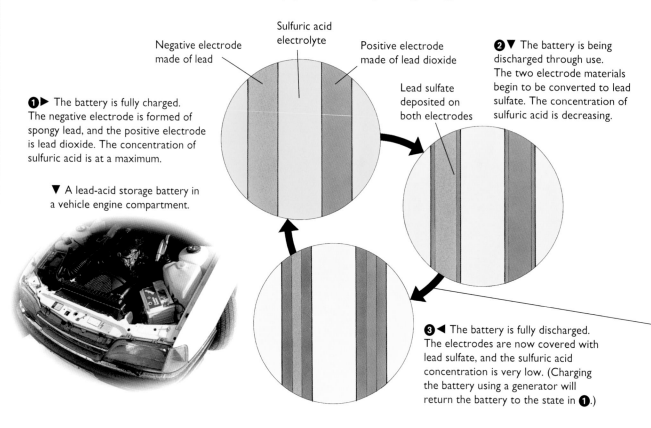

Negative electrode made of lead

Sulfuric acid electrolyte

Positive electrode made of lead dioxide

Lead sulfate deposited on both electrodes

❶▶ The battery is fully charged. The negative electrode is formed of spongy lead, and the positive electrode is lead dioxide. The concentration of sulfuric acid is at a maximum.

▼ A lead-acid storage battery in a vehicle engine compartment.

❷▼ The battery is being discharged through use. The two electrode materials begin to be converted to lead sulfate. The concentration of sulfuric acid is decreasing.

❸◀ The battery is fully discharged. The electrodes are now covered with lead sulfate, and the sulfuric acid concentration is very low. (Charging the battery using a generator will return the battery to the state in **❶**.)

EQUATION: Discharging (using) a lead-acid battery

Lead + lead dioxide + sulfuric acid ⇨ lead sulfate + water

$$Pb(s) + PbO_2(s) + 2H_2SO_4(aq) \Rightarrow 2PbSO_4(s) + 2H_2O(l)$$

EQUATION: Charging a lead-acid battery

Lead sulfate + water ⇨ lead + lead dioxide + sulfuric acid

$$2PbSO_4(s) + 2H_2O(l) \Rightarrow Pb(s) + PbO_2(s) + 2H_2SO_4(aq)$$

How lead–acid batteries work

Lead–acid batteries are the most commonly used form of vehicle battery. To work as an electrical battery, each of the cells inside it must have two electrodes made of electrically conducting materials. These must be bathed in a liquid that can conduct electricity as well as help the battery store electricity. This material is called an electrolyte.

The electrodes, or plates, in lead–acid batteries are designed to have a large surface area. This allows the charge stored as chemical energy to be converted quickly into electrical energy. Half of the electrodes are made from a lead alloy covered in a paste of lead dioxide; the other half are made simply of lead alloy (known as "spongy" lead). All the plates are bathed in dilute sulfuric acid.

When a charge is drawn from the battery, a chemical reaction occurs between the plates and the sulfate ions of the electrolyte that changes the lead dioxide into lead sulfate.

When the battery is charged (perhaps from a vehicle generator), and a current passed through the battery, a chemical reaction occurs that turns the lead sulfate on the plates into lead and lead dioxide and returns the sulfate to the electrolyte, thus increasing the concentration of the acid.

When a load is applied to the battery, the reaction reverses, the lead sulfate coatings re-form and the sulfuric acid is used up.

This process can be repeated many times, giving the secondary battery a useful life of many years of constant service.

battery: a number of electrochemical cells placed in series. A 12V battery contains 6 cells, each providing 2V.

cell: a vessel containing two electrodes and an electrolyte that can act as an electrical conductor.

current: an electric current is produced by a flow of electrons through a conducting solid or ions through a conducting liquid.

electrolyte: a solution that conducts electricity.

ion: an atom, or group of atoms, that has gained or lost one or more electrons and so developed an electrical charge. Ions behave differently from electrically neutral atoms and molecules. They can move in an electric field, and they can also bind strongly to solvent molecules such as water. Positively charged ions are called cations; negatively charged ions are called anions. Ions carry electrical current through solutions.

Positive electrode made of lead dioxide

Sulfuric acid electrolyte

▶ This diagram shows the arrangement of lead and lead oxide plates. Notice that each cell is connected in series to the next through conductors at the top of the plates.

Negative electrode made of lead

Lead and the body

Lead is a heavy, unreactive substance. These very properties have been used for the benefit of health, and they have also caused major health problems.

Although lead has many advantages outside the body, such as protecting people from overdoses of harmful radiation, it has become widely known in recent years for its harmful effects inside the body. Examples of this are given on these pages and on pages 32 and 33. Lead is by no means the only substance that can harm the body; but because it was used so widely in fuels and paints, its effects were readily noticed.

Lead in cosmetics of the past

Body painting was the earliest use of cosmetics, meant to protect the body from evil spirits. Many of the original natural cosmetics also helped to protect the wearer from flies. As a result, cosmetics were most often applied to the areas around the eyes. One of the most common cosmetics was a white pigment made from white lead. The ancient civilizations of the Middle East used to paint eyelashes and eyebrows with a black paste that included lead sulfide (galena) and soot. Later, the Romans made white face powder using white lead. It was extremely poisonous.

The modern art of makeup developed in Europe, especially in France and in Venice, Italy. Venetians made a specially desirable form of paste known as cerise. It had the effect of making the skin of the face white. It, too, was made from white lead.

People knew that using lead on the face would eventually result in lead poisoning, causing deterioration of complexion, baldness and eventually death. Nevertheless, so great was the desire to look beautiful that many poisoned themselves through this particularly dangerous form of makeup.

▶ In Roman times, and despite being known as a poison, lead was added to drinks because it enhanced their flavor.

Lead poisoning

From ancient times, pottery workers were known to suffer from lead poisoning because of breathing in lead fumes and handling lead glazes. At the beginning of the 20th century, lead was so widely used for industrial processes that researchers found 77 occupations at risk from lead poisoning. Such evidence began to make protection from harmful substances seem necessary.

Lead is absorbed very slowly. Unfortunately, the body has no natural way of getting rid of any lead that is absorbed, so any lead taken in as fumes or in food, or in liquids, simply builds up in the body, especially in the liver and kidneys.

People suffering from lead poisoning lose their appetite, start to be sick and may develop convulsions. In severe cases the brain is damaged and death may follow.

The most important sources of lead poisoning are thought to be caused by lead in some drinking water supplies (especially in soft-water areas) and in vehicle exhausts.

Studies show that children are particularly vulnerable to lead poisoning. This knowledge has resulted in the replacement of lead with copper water pipes, the removal of lead from domestic paints and the change from leaded to unleaded fuel.

EQUATION: How lead dissolves in water

Lead + soft water + dissolved oxygen ⇨ lead hydroxide

$$2Pb(s) \quad + \quad 2H_2O(l) \quad + \quad O_2(g) \quad ⇨ \quad 2Pb(OH)_2(aq)$$

Lead shield

radiation: the exchange of energy with the surroundings through the transmission of waves or particles of energy. Radiation is a form of energy transfer that can happen through space; no intervening medium is required (as would be the case for conduction and convection).

radioactive: emitting radiation or particles from the nucleus of its atoms.

X-rays: a form of very shortwave radiation.

Lead protects the body from radiation

X-rays, which are produced when charged particles collide, are a form of radiation whose waves have a much shorter wavelength than that of visible light.

How well X-rays can pass through a material depends on the density of the atoms of the material. Bones, for example, are very dense and block most radiation, and this is what causes their X-ray image to appear white. Tissue blocks less radiation and appears darker on the film. Lead is composed of large, closely packed atoms that will absorb all X-rays.

One common use of lead is therefore as a shield against radiation, for example, to protect those who make X-ray pictures in hospitals and dental offices. It is also used in nuclear power stations and in the containers used to transport radioactive materials.

◀ Lead is made of closely packed large and heavy atoms. This makes it very difficult for radiation to pass through it.

Lead in fuels

We use gas in most of the world's engines. Gas is made from refined crude oil, which is a compound of carbon. The fuel is "atomized" and sprayed into the engine cylinders along with air. The piston then rises in the cylinder and compresses the mixture, causing it to get hot.

As the air is being compressed, and before a spark is generated by the sparkplug, the mixture may explode. This is called preignition, and it is noticed as a knocking sound inside the engine.

The numbers used to describe the quality of the fuel are octane numbers. Commonly the octane number varies between 79 and 91. This number describes the way the fuel can resist "knocking."

When engines knock, it means that the mixture has exploded while the piston is still traveling up the cylinder, not when it has just passed the top of its stroke, as is meant to happen. By exploding at the wrong time, the engine become both noisy and less efficient, and so consumes more fuel.

Compounds of lead (tetraethyl lead, $Pb(C_2H_5)_4$) were traditionally added to the fuel to stop the mixture from exploding prematurely. This meant that engines ran more efficiently. This was a good example of how a simple chemical treatment provided a cheap solution to a problem. However, because it has now been realized that lead can be toxic in the environment, this use of lead is now being phased out. Instead, the engines have had to be redesigned so that they do not knock even when lead additives are not present.

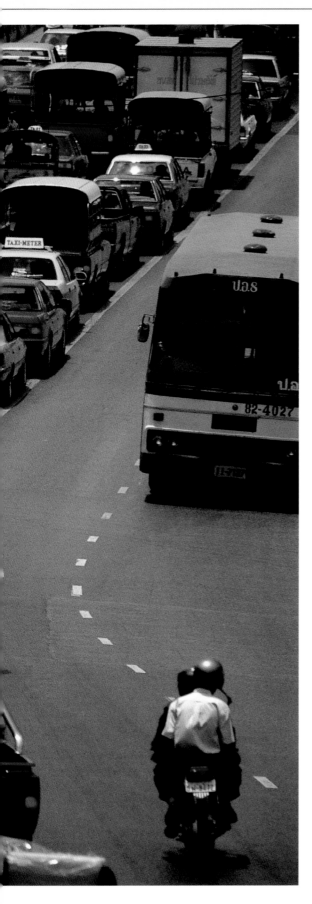

atomized: broken up into a very fine mist. The term is used in connection with sprays and engine fuel systems.

mixture: a material that can be separated into two or more substances using physical means.

octane: one of the substances contained in fuel.

Catalytic converters

These work by passing the spent exhaust fumes from the engine over a fine mesh coated with platinum or other material. This makes the gases turn into less poisonous forms. However, if a catalytic converter were used with leaded fuel, then the lead in the exhaust would coat the mesh and make the converter inoperable. This is why converters can only be used with lead-free fuel.

◀ The first country to change from leaded to unleaded fuel was the United States, following a ruling by the Environmental Protection Agency in 1985. Most other industrial world countries have followed the same pattern, so that it is now less common to find leaded fuel on sale.

▼ The oxidation of gases in internal combustion engines.

Sparkplug

Valves

Cylinder

Piston

Tin

Tin is a relatively rare, silvery white, soft metal with a low melting point (232°C). It is mostly found as tin oxide, cassiterite, in veins that are close to igneous rocks (the same conditions that gave rise to lead deposits, see page 7). Tin compounds were probably deposited in these veins by hot fluids rising above molten magma.

Tin is a very soft and weak metal, so it is never used on its own. Tin is also very brittle; a bar of tin will break up into sharp crystals if bent as well as making a high pitched sound like crying.

The main use of tin has traditionally been as a plating on steel (see page 38), utilizing the noncorrosive properties of the metal.

However, tin has many other uses, especially as an alloy. Although tin is a weak metal on its own, an alloy that includes tin is typically much harder than one without it. There are other advantages, too, such as making the alloy easier to cast. Tin is found in some brass, bronze and pewter.

The low melting point of tin makes it a useful component of solder and for preparing alloys that have low melting points. For this reason, it can be used in fire-detection systems.

Ore deposits

Tin, like many other poorly reactive metals, such as tungsten, copper and silver, is formed in the metamorphic zones surrounding ancient magma chambers. It was present in the hydrothermal fluids that rose up from the magma chambers as they cooled during the last stages of volcanic activity. The fluids flowed into fissures that had been produced as the magma chambers domed up the overlying rocks. As the fluids rose in the fissures, they cooled, and a wide variety of minerals solidified as the temperature dropped below their various melting points. Tin-bearing lodes are normally found making a ring of fissures over a magma chamber.

The only lode deposits to have been found are in Cornwall, England, and Bolivia. These rich lodes are mined and the tin processed by direct smelting. The type of mining involved is shown on these pages.

Elsewhere tin is mined as placer deposits, that is, deposits of sand and clay that contain tin that has been eroded from lodes and transported by streams. These are very low-grade deposits and have to be processed over a number of stages.

◀ Cornish tin mines during the time when they were at full production during the last century.

Mining for lode tin

This diagram shows how hot fluids rising up from molten magma injected themselves into the rock surrounding the magma.

To recover this ore, deep shafts were sunk, following the near vertical directions of the deposits. The veins were typically very narrow, perhaps no more than a meter wide, something like sheets of material. The network of shafts and horizontal tunnels (adits) developed in a mine were designed to reach these mineral sheets from a number of places.

Lode ore contains a variety of impurities including tungsten, sulfur and arsenic, most of which can be removed by a stage of roasting before final smelting. Roasting arsenic-containing ores was a hazardous process.

igneous rock: a rock that has solidified from molten rock, either volcanic lava on the Earth's surface or molten magma deep underground. In either case the rock develops a network of interlocking crystals.

lode: a number of veins of a metal found close together.

magma: the molten rock that forms a balloon-shaped chamber in the rock below a volcano. It is fed by rock moving upward from below the crust.

metamorphic rock: formed either from igneous or sedimentary rocks by heat or pressure. Metamorphic rocks form deep inside mountains during periods of mountain building. They result from the remelting of rocks, during which process crystals are able to grow. Metamorphic rocks often show signs of banding and partial melting.

oxide: a compound that includes oxygen and one other element.

reduction: the removal of oxygen from a substance.

▶ A 19th-century deep tin mine.

Winding gear and steam engine house

Waste rock

Processing sheds

Abandoned shaft used for ventilation

Vertical shafts to connect the tunnels

Horizontal tunnels at various depths to reach the veins (lodes)

Metamorphic zone where the veins containing metal compounds are found

Granite, the once-molten source of the heat that produced the ore veins

▼ Tin mining in Britain has now all but stopped because the world price for tin is too low to make deep lode mining profitable. Many of the mines are now in a ruined state. Compare this modern picture with the etching on the left.

EQUATION: Refining tin by reducing the tin ore in furnace containing coke

Tin dioxide + carbon (coke) ⇨ liquid tin + carbon dioxide

$$SnO_2(s) \quad + \quad C(s) \quad \Rightarrow \quad Sn(s) \quad + \quad CO_2(g)$$

Placer tin mining

Four-fifths of the world's tin is obtained from placer deposits. Most placer deposits use high-pressure hoses to wash out the tin from deposits, or they use some form of excavator to dredge it from under the sea.

Placer deposits contain very low concentrations of tin that must be concentrated before they can be refined. Tin ore is a dense material, and so the first stage of concentration is to wash it over ridges called riffles in a sluice box (see the picture on this page). The tin ore settles out and the other waste materials are washed away.

Unlike many other concentration techniques (such as that for lead shown on page 10), a relatively simple method such as sluicing concentrates the ore so that about three-quarters is tin oxide. This allows the placer ore to be smelted directly.

After smelting, the final impurities are removed from the tin by remelting and sometimes also by electrolysis. In the remelting method advantage is taken of the low melting point of tin. As the impure tin is heated, it melts and can be run off before the impurities begin to melt.

► Tin mining using placer deposits in Thailand. The working of such large deposits can cause great environmental damage unless care is taken with the waste materials.

Also...

The major tin-producing countries are Malaysia, Indonesia, Bolivia, Thailand, Russia, China and Brazil. The demand for tin has dropped in recent years as aluminum cans have supplanted steel cans. This change in use of metals has had a very severe impact on some developing world nations, depriving them of one of their sources of income.

Tin plating

As soon as tin metal is exposed to the air, it develops a strong, gastight coating that prevents it from being corroded further. Although iron is next to tin in the reactivity series, the oxide coating that develops on iron is porous, which is why iron rusts. Thus tin (oxide) behaves very differently from iron. The low melting point of tin also means that it is easy to run sheet steel through a bath of tin without any fear that the steel might melt. These twin advantages have given tin its major use: as a way of protecting steel.

▲ Perhaps the world's largest tin object, the Margate Elephant, in New Jersey, is as high as a six story building and weighs 90 tons. It was built to attract tourists; its frame is made of wood, but its skin is made of tin to prevent corrosion in this exposed seaside environment.

▼ Tin plating is produced by pulling sheet steel through a bath of molten tin. This produces a coating on both sides of the steel.

Food containers

The advantage of tin is best seen in its use for food containers. Many foods contain organic acids. However, tin remains unreactive and so can be used for the inside of food cans because the food will not corrode the can. Tin plating was developed as a means of preserving moist food so that it could be taken to military forces when on active service. The French were among the first to try to invent a preserving process. In 1795 a Parisian chef, Nicolas Appert, invented the canning process. However, as tin-coated steel had not at that time been invented, his process actually involved preserving cooked food in bottles.

Bottles are not a good means of carrying food because of the risk of breakage. A new material had to be found. The tin-coated metal can was invented in Britain in 1810, and it was at this time that the word canning came into general use.

The value of the tin can was that the strength and cheapness of thin steel could be complemented by the corrosion resistance of soft tin. Plating the steel (which had to be done both inside and out) prevented the steel from rusting. The steel plate was curled into a cylinder and the seam made tight using a solder join. The top and bottom of the can could be fixed on with a press.

REACTIVITY SERIES	
Element	*Reactivity*
potassium	*most reactive*
sodium	
calcium	
magnesium	
aluminum	
manganese	
chromium	
zinc	
iron	
cadmium	
tin	
lead	
copper	
mercury	
silver	
gold	
platinum	*least reactive*

corrosive: a substance, either an acid or an alkali, that *rapidly* attacks a wide range of other substances.

plating: adding a thin coat of one material to another to make it resistant to corrosion.

◀ Metals can be placed in order of how vigorously they react in a list called a reactivity series. Tin is below iron in the reactivity series. Therefore exposed iron will always corrode when placed in a damp environment with tin. This is why steel cans rust badly as soon as they become scratched. It is not just the iron rusting; it is also encouraged to rust faster by the presence of the tin.

The disadvantage of using tin plate

Tin is plated onto iron or steel to protect it from corrosion, but it is only good if it remains unscratched. The reason you often see rusting cans is that tin is below steel (iron) in the reactivity series, so that when the steel is exposed by scratching, the steel corrodes at the expense of the tin, and the tin doesn't protect the steel at all. This is an important reason why aluminum containers have replaced tin-plated ones in recent years.

▶ A nail with a small tin collar has been placed in water. After a few days the nail is heavily rusted, but the tin is unaffected. This shows that tin speeds up the corrosion of steel and shows why tin-plated objects are only protected provided the tin remains unscratched.

Also...

Tin-plating is not the ideal way of protecting food. However, it was the best way for 150 years given the technology available until recently. Thus tin cans dominated the food-preservation market for 150 years because aluminum could not be produced cheaply.

Pewter and bronze

Pewter was originally an alloy of 40% lead and 60% tin. Because of the toxic effects of lead, modern pewter mostly contains tin with about 8% antimony as a hardening agent.

Pewter, which is a dark gray color, was first made by the Romans, who used the tin from mines in Cornwall, England. As a result, England became an important center for pewter.

Because it is quite soft, pewter was easily worked both by hammering and by turning on a lathe. It was used until the last century for all manner of goods, from utensils for the kitchen to goblets and chalices used in churches and monasteries. Pewter found its way to many parts of the world, and much of the antique pewter found in North America and Australasia was made in England.

Since the 19th century, when pewter was replaced by more durable metals and ceramics, pewter has mainly been used for decoration.

▲ Pewter was widely used because it was soft and easily worked. However, the high lead content meant that when it was used in articles intended for food or drink, some lead could be dissolved and produce a health hazard. Thus all modern pewter is lead free.

Copper

Tin

▲ A bronze bell in Fort Sutter, Sacramento, California.

◄ Snail-eating utensils cast in pewter.

Bronze

Bronze is an alloy of copper and tin. Up to 10% of tin is normally used. Bronze has been used for decorative metal objects and also for coins. It was one of the earliest metal alloys made, giving rise to the first metal-working age, known as the Bronze Age, over three thousand years ago. Bronze Age people, however, did not know about alloying metals but used copper ores that contained tin impurities.

Bronzes are important because they are strong, they do not wear away easily (when used, for example, in gear wheels), and they resist saltwater corrosion. The rule is, the more tin there is in the alloy, the harder and more brittle it becomes. Bronzes with up to one-twelfth tin are used mainly for sheets, wire and coins; those with one-eighth tin are used mainly for gears, bearings and ships in exposed locations. When bronze contains up to one-fifth tin, it is used for gear wheels; and with up to one-quarter tin, bronze is used to make bells.

Also... special bronzes

A wide range of specialized bronzes are used, each with its own distinctive properties. These are produced by alloying with more elements. Phosphor bronze, for example, is commonly used for bearings in machines or engines where shafts continually rotate. Phosphor bronze is made by adding one-third of 1% of phosphorus to the alloy.

Silicon bronze is a strong metal, used in places where there is a great danger of corrosion, such as a chemical plant. This alloy contains up to 3% silicon.

Solder

Soldering is a process of joining two pieces of metal together with a filler metal. Soldering metals have to be chosen to alloy with the metals they are joining and so provide a strong joint.

The composition of the solder is also designed to have a low melting point, so that it can be applied easily without damaging the metals being soldered.

Common solders are mixtures, or alloys, of lead and tin. Both lead and tin have low melting points, but a mixture of the two is stronger and has a lower melting point than either metal. Some materials, such as wires, are tin plated to make soldering easier.

The most common use of lead-tin soldering is to join copper wires or pipes.

To make a soldered joint

The use of lead solder relies on the way that a liquid will pull itself into a small space, called capillary action. The metal surfaces will only join if they are clean, so in general the tarnished surface is scraped away using steel wool, and the metal left bright and shiny. A material called a flux is then spread over the metals to be joined to prevent them from tarnishing again as they are heated.

For joining wires a soldering iron is used, and the solder has small rods of flux embedded in it. For soldering larger items, such as pipes, the heat has to be applied by a source such as a blowtorch. It is important that the heat is applied evenly so that the solder can run quickly and smoothly.

▼ Copper pipework is joined by solder. A flux is applied to the surfaces to be joined to prevent them from oxidizing in the heat before the solder melts.

These ridges contain solder reservoirs. When the joint is heated with a blowtorch, the solder melts. A close fit ensures that capillary action causes the solder to flow evenly throughout the joint.

▶ The most commonly used solder consists of 50% tin and 50% lead. Solders containing a higher proportion of tin (say two-thirds tin, one-third lead) can be applied at a lower temperature but tend to be more brittle.

Lead solder and printed circuits

A printed circuit is an arrangement of electronic components, such as transistors and resistors, on a supporting board that is already printed with circuit wires.

The connections of the circuit are made with very thin layers of copper held in place by a glue. Too much heat and the glue will melt and the copper conductors will fall off the printed circuit board. The electronic components are equally delicate, and heat may easily crack them.

The key to making mass-produced printed circuits, found in everything from computers to washing machines, is to join the components to the copper on the board speedily and with as little heat as possible.

To do this the components are all pushed through holes in the board, and then the copper side is exposed. The protruding component wires are then soldered to the copper by passing them through an automatic soldering machine that applies just the right amount of solder for just the right length of time to make the correct joint before the board or components have the time to heat up too much.

capillary action: the tendency for a liquid to be sucked into small spaces, such as between objects and through narrow-pore tubes. The force to do this comes from surface tension.

flux: a material used to make it easier for a liquid to flow. A flux dissolves metal oxides and so prevents a metal from oxidizing while being heated.

tarnish: a coating that develops as a result of the reaction between a metal and substances in the air. The most common form of tarnishing is a very thin transparent oxide coating.

▼ A section of circuit board showing the use of solder to connect components to the printed circuit.

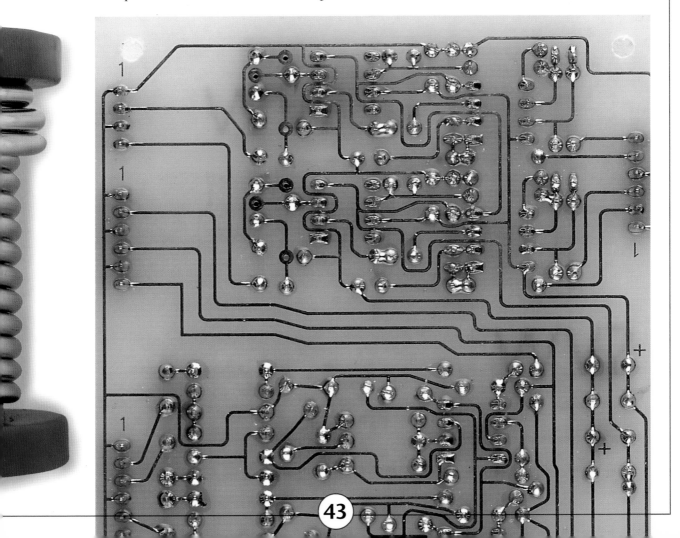

Key facts about...

Lead

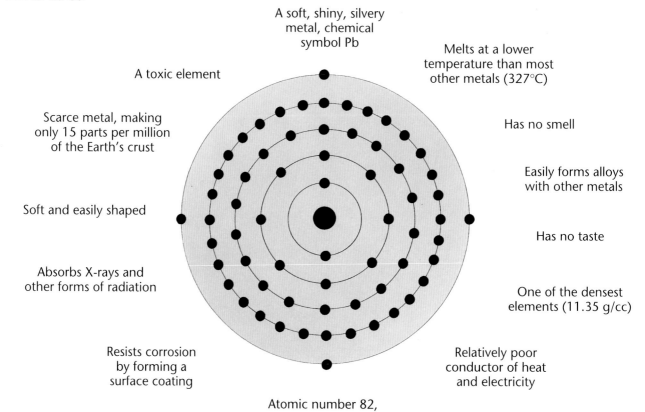

A soft, shiny, silvery metal, chemical symbol Pb

A toxic element

Melts at a lower temperature than most other metals (327°C)

Scarce metal, making only 15 parts per million of the Earth's crust

Has no smell

Easily forms alloys with other metals

Soft and easily shaped

Has no taste

Absorbs X-rays and other forms of radiation

One of the densest elements (11.35 g/cc)

Resists corrosion by forming a surface coating

Relatively poor conductor of heat and electricity

Atomic number 82, atomic weight about 207

SHELL DIAGRAMS
The shell diagrams on these two pages are representations of an atom of each element. The total number of electrons is shown in the relevant orbitals, or shells, around the central nucleus.

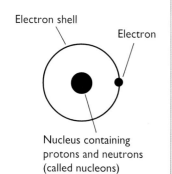

Electron shell

Electron

Nucleus containing protons and neutrons (called nucleons)

▶ Many Roman "bronze" coins were made of alloys of varying proportions of copper with tin, lead and zinc. Many of these alloys have proven to be resistant to corrosion and as a result can be in very good condition despite having been buried for over 2,000 years.

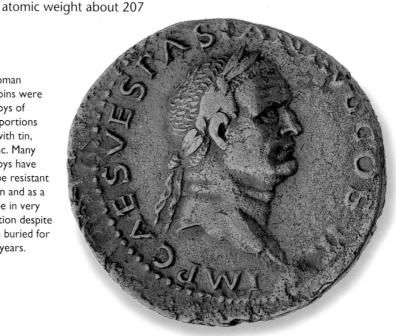

Tin

A soft, shiny, silvery metal, chemical symbol Sn

A weak metal that cannot be used alone

Good conductor of heat and electricity

Has no smell

Does not tarnish when exposed to the air

Easily forms alloys with other metals

Has no taste

Density 7.3 g/cc

Melts at 232°C

Atomic number 50, atomic weight about 119

When a colorless solution of lead nitrate is added to a similarly colorless solution of potassium iodide, a thick yellow precipitate of lead iodide forms.

The Periodic Table

The Periodic Table sets out the relationships among the elements of the Universe. According to the Periodic Table, certain elements fall into groups. The pattern of these groups has, in the past, allowed scientists to predict elements that had not at that time been discovered. It can still be used today to predict the properties of unfamiliar elements.

The Periodic Table was first described by a Russian teacher, Dmitry Ivanovich Mendeleev, between 1869 and 1870. He was interested in writing a chemistry textbook and wanted to show his students that there were certain patterns in the elements that had been discovered. So he set out the elements (of which there were 57 at the time) according to their known properties. On the assumption that there was pattern to the elements, he left blank spaces where elements seemed to be missing. Using this first version of the Periodic Table, he was able to predict in detail the chemical and physical properties of elements that had not yet been discovered. Other scientists began to look for the missing elements, and they soon found them.

GROUP

Metals
Metalloids (semimetals)
Nonmetals

Transition metals

Lanthanide metals

Actinoid metals

Hydrogen did not seem to fit into the table, and so he placed it in a box on its own. Otherwise the elements were all placed horizontally. When an element was reached with properties similar to the first one in the top row, a second row was started. By following this rule, similarities among the elements can be found by reading up and down. By reading across the rows, the elements progressively increase their atomic number. This number indicates the number of positively charged particles (protons) in the nucleus of each atom. This is also the number of negatively charged particles (electrons) in the atom.

The chemical properties of an element depend on the number of electrons in the outermost shell.

Atoms can form compounds by sharing electrons in their outermost shells. This explains why atoms with a full set of electrons (like helium, an inert gas) are unreactive, whereas atoms with an incomplete electron shell (such as chlorine) are very reactive. Elements can also combine by the complete transfer of electrons from metals to nonmetals, and the compounds formed contain ions.

Radioactive elements lose particles from their nucleus and electrons from their surrounding shells. As a result they change their atomic number and so become new elements.

Key:
- Atomic (proton) number — 13
- Symbol — Al
- Name — Aluminum
- Approximate relative atomic mass — 27

3	4	5	6	7	0
					2 He Helium 4
5 B Boron 11	6 C Carbon 12	7 N Nitrogen 14	8 O Oxygen 16	9 F Fluorine 19	10 Ne Neon 20
13 Al Aluminum 27	14 Si Silicon 28	15 P Phosphorus 31	16 S Sulfur 32	17 Cl Chlorine 35	18 Ar Argon 40

	28 Ni Nickel 59	29 Cu Copper 64	30 Zn Zinc 65	31 Ga Gallium 70	32 Ge Germanium 73	33 As Arsenic 75	34 Se Selenium 79	35 Br Bromine 80	36 Kr Krypton 84
	46 Pd Palladium 106	47 Ag Silver 108	48 Cd Cadmium 112	49 In Indium 115	50 Sn Tin 119	51 Sb Antimony 122	52 Te Tellurium 128	53 I Iodine 127	54 Xe Xenon 131
	78 Pt Platinum 195	79 Au Gold 197	80 Hg Mercury 201	81 Tl Thallium 204	82 Pb Lead 207	83 Bi Bismuth 209	84 Po Polonium (209)	85 At Astatine (210)	86 Rn Radon (222)

	62 Sm Samarium 150	63 Eu Europium 152	64 Gd Gadolinium 157	65 Tb Terbium 159	66 Dy Dysprosium 163	67 Ho Holmium 165	68 Er Erbium 167	69 Tm Thulium 169	70 Yb Ytterbium 173
	94 Pu Plutonium (244)	95 Am Americium (243)	96 Cm Curium (247)	97 Bk Berkelium (247)	98 Cf Californium (251)	99 Es Einsteinium (252)	100 Fm Fermium (257)	101 Md Mendelevium (258)	102 No Nobelium (259)

Understanding equations

As you read through this book, you will notice that many pages contain equations using symbols. If you are not familiar with these symbols, read this page. Symbols make it easy for chemists to write out the reactions that are occurring in a way that allows a better understanding of the processes involved.

Symbols for the elements

The basis of the modern use of symbols for elements dates back to the 19th century. At this time a shorthand was developed using the first letter of the element wherever possible. Thus "O" stands for oxygen, "H" stands for hydrogen

and so on. However, if we were to use only the first letter, then there could be some confusion. For example, nitrogen and nickel would both use the symbols N. To overcome this problem, many elements are symbolized using the first two letters of their full name, and the second letter is not in capitals. Thus although nitrogen is N, nickel becomes Ni. Not all symbols come from the English name; many use the Latin name instead. This is why, for example, gold is not G but Au (for the Latin *aurum*) and sodium has the symbol Na, from the Latin *natrium*.

Compounds of elements are made by combining letters. Thus the molecule carbon

---

Written and symbolic equations

In this book important chemical equations are briefly stated in words (these are called word equations) and are then shown in their symbolic form along with the states.

What reaction the equation illustrates

Written equation

Symbol equation

EQUATION: The formation of calcium hydroxide

Calcium oxide + water ⇨ calcium hydroxide

$$CaO(s) \quad + \quad H_2O(l) \quad ⇨ \quad Ca(OH)_2(aq)$$

heated

Sometimes you will find an additional description below the symbolic equation.

Symbol showing the state: *s* is for solid, *l* is for liquid, *g* is for gas and *aq* is for aqueous.

Diagrams

Some of the equations are shown as graphic representations.

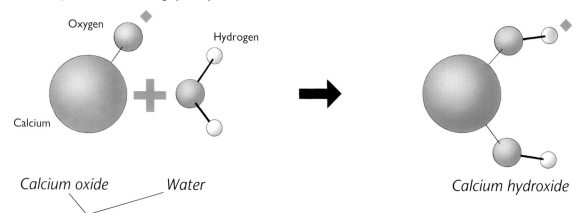

Oxygen

Hydrogen

Calcium

Calcium oxide   *Water*

Calcium hydroxide

Sometimes the written equation is broken up and put below the relevant stages in the graphic representation.

monoxide is CO. By using letters that are not capitals for the second letter of an element, it is possible to show that cobalt, symbol Co, is not the same as the molecule carbon monoxide, CO.

However, the letters can be made to do much more than this. In many molecules, atoms combine in unequal numbers. So, for example, carbon dioxide has one atom of carbon for every two of oxygen. This is shown by using the number 2 beside the oxygen, and the symbol becomes CO_2.

In practice, some groups of atoms combine as a unit with other substances. Thus, for example, calcium bicarbonate (one of the compounds used in some antacid pills) is written $Ca(HCO_3)_2$. This shows that the part of the substance inside the brackets reacts as a unit, and the "2" outside the brackets shows the presence of two such units.

Some substances attract water molecules to themselves. To show this a dot is used. Thus the blue-colored form of copper sulfate is written $CuSO_4.5H_2O$. In this case five molecules of water attract to one copper sulfate. When you see the dot, you know that this water can be driven off by heating; it is part of the crystal structure.

In a reaction substances change by rearranging the combinations of atoms. The way they change is shown by using the chemical symbols, placing those that will react (the starting materials, or reactants) on the left and the products of the reaction on the right. Between the two, chemists use an arrow to show which way the reaction is occurring.

It is possible to describe a reaction in words. This gives a word equation. Word equations are used throughout this book. However, it is easier to understand what is happening by using an equation containing symbols. These are also given in many places. They are not used when the equations are very complex.

In any equation both sides balance; that is, there must be an equal number of like atoms on both sides of the arrow. When you try to write down reactions, you, too, must balance your equation; you cannot have a few atoms left over at the end!

The symbols in brackets are abbreviations for the physical state of each substance taking part, so that (s) is used for solid, (l) for liquid, (g) for gas and (aq) for an aqueous solution, that is, a solution of a substance dissolved in water.

Atoms and ions
Each sphere represents a particle of an element. A particle can be an atom or an ion. Each atom or ion is associated with other atoms or ions through bonds – forces of attraction. The size of the particles and the nature of the bonds can be extremely important in determining the nature of the reaction or the properties of the compound.

This indicates that the compound is ionic.

Sodium

▶ This represents a unit of sodium bicarbonate ($NaHCO_3$).

The term "unit" is sometimes used to simplify the representation of a combination of ions.

Chemical symbols, equations and diagrams
The arrangement of any molecule or compound can be shown in one of the two ways below, depending on which gives the clearer picture. The left-hand diagram is called a ball-and-stick diagram because it uses rods and spheres to show the structure of the material. This example shows water, H_2O. There are two hydrogen atoms and one oxygen atom.

Bond shown by "stick"

Colors too
The colors of each of the particles help differentiate the elements involved. The diagram can then be matched to the written and symbolic equation given with the diagram. In the case above, oxygen is red and hydrogen is gray.

Glossary of technical terms

alloy: a mixture of a metal and various other elements.

atomized: broken up into a very fine mist. The term is used in connection with sprays and engine fuel systems.

battery: a number of electrochemical cells placed in series. A 12V battery contains 6 cells, each providing 2V.

bond: chemical bonding is either a transfer or sharing of electrons by two or more atoms. There are a number of types of chemical bond, some very strong (such as covalent bonds), others weak (such as hydrogen bonds). Chemical bonds form because the linked molecule is more stable than the unlinked atoms from which it formed. For example, the hydrogen molecule (H_2) is more stable than single atoms of hydrogen, which is why hydrogen gas is always found as molecules of two hydrogen atoms.

capillary action: the tendency for a liquid to be sucked into small spaces, such as between objects and through narrow-pore tubes. The force to do this comes from surface tension.

catalyst: a substance that speeds up a chemical reaction but itself remains unaltered at the end of the reaction.

cell: a vessel containing two electrodes and an electrolyte that can act as an electrical conductor.

ceramic: a material based on clay minerals which has been heated so that it has chemically hardened.

corrosion: the *slow* decay of a substance resulting from contact with gases and liquids in the environment. The term is often applied to metals. Rust is the corrosion of iron.

corrosive: a substance, either an acid or an alkali, that *rapidly* attacks a wide range of other substances.

current: an electric current is produced by a flow of electrons through a conducting solid or ions through a conducting liquid.

decompose: to break down a substance (for example, by heat or with the aid of a catalyst) into simpler components. In such a chemical reaction only one substance is involved.

density: the mass per unit volume (e.g., g/cc).

dissolve: to break down a substance in a solution without reacting.

electrode: a conductor that forms one terminal of a cell.

electrolysis: an electrical-chemical process that uses an electric current to cause the breakup of a compound and the movement of metal ions in a solution. The process happens in many natural situations (as for example in rusting) and is also commonly used in industry for purifying (refining) metals or for plating metal objects with a fine, even metal coating.

electrolyte: a solution that conducts electricity.

electron: a tiny, negatively charged particle that is part of an atom. The flow of electrons through a solid material such as a wire produces an electric current.

flux: a material used to make it easier for a liquid to flow. A flux dissolves metal oxides and so prevents a metal from oxidizing while being heated.

gangue: the unwanted material in an ore.

hydrothermal: a process in which hot water is involved. It is usually used in the context of rock formation because hot water and other fluids sent outward from liquid magmas are important carriers of metals and the minerals that form gemstones.

igneous rock: a rock that has solidified from molten rock, either volcanic lava on the Earth's surface or molten magma deep underground. In either case the rock develops a network of interlocking crystals.

inert: nonreactive.

infrared radiation: a form of light radiation in which the wavelength of the waves is slightly longer than visible light. Most heat radiation is in the infrared band.

ion: an atom, or group of atoms, that has gained or lost one or more electrons and so developed an electrical charge. Ions behave differently from electrically neutral atoms and molecules. They can move in an electric field, and they can also bind strongly to solvent molecules such as water. Positively charged ions are called cations; negatively charged ions are called anions. Ions carry electrical current through solutions.

lode: a number of veins of a metal found close together.

magma: the molten rock that forms a balloon-shaped chamber in the rock below a volcano. It is fed by rock moving upward from below the crust.

metamorphic rock: formed either from igneous or sedimentary rocks by heat or pressure. Metamorphic rocks form deep inside mountains during periods of mountain building. They result from the remelting of rocks, during which process crystals are able to grow. Metamorphic rocks often show signs of banding and partial melting.

mineral: a solid substance made of just one element or chemical compound. Calcite is a mineral because it consists only of calcium carbonate; halite is a mineral because it contains only sodium chloride; quartz is a mineral because it consists of only silicon dioxide.

mixture: a material that can be separated into two or more substances using physical means.

octane: one of the substances contained in fuel.

ore: a rock containing enough of a useful substance to make mining it worthwhile.

oxidation: a reaction in which the oxidizing agent removes electrons. (Note that oxidizing agents do not have to contain oxygen.)

oxide: a compound that includes oxygen and one other element.

pigment: any solid material used to give a liquid a color.

plating: adding a thin coat of one material to another to make it resistant to corrosion.

precious metal: silver, gold, platinum, iridium and palladium. Each is prized for its rarity. This category is the equivalent of gemstones for minerals.

pyrite: "mineral of fire." This name comes from the fact that pyrite (iron sulfide) will give off sparks if struck with a stone.

pyrometallurgy: refining a metal from its ore using heat. A blast furnace or smelter is the main equipment used.

radiation: the exchange of energy with the surroundings through the transmission of waves or particles of energy. Radiation is a form of energy transfer that can happen through space; no intervening medium is required (as would be the case for conduction and convection).

radioactive: emitting radiation or particles from the nucleus of its atoms.

reduction: the removal of oxygen from a substance.

reducing agent: a substance that gives electrons to another substance. Carbon is a reducing agent when heated with lead oxide.

refractive index: the property of a transparent material that controls the angle at which total internal reflection will occur. The greater the refractive index, the more reflective the material.

slag: a mixture of substances that are waste products of a furnace. Most slags are composed mainly of silicates.

sulfide: a sulfur compound that contains no oxygen.

tarnish: a coating that develops as a result of the reaction between a metal and substances in the air. The most common form of tarnishing is a very thin transparent oxide coating.

toxic: poisonous enough to cause death.

vein: a mineral deposit different from, and usually cutting across, the surrounding rocks. Most mineral and metal-bearing veins are deposits filling fractures. The veins were filled by hot, mineral-rich waters rising upward from liquid volcanic magma. They are important sources of many metals, such as silver and gold, and also minerals such as gemstones. Veins are usually narrow and were best suited to hand-mining. They are less exploited in the modern machine age.

viscous: slow-moving, syrupy. A liquid that has a low viscosity is said to be mobile.

X-rays: a form of very shortwave radiation.

Master Index